WINGS No.9

BOMBS G(

Modern Aircraft Ordnance in Action

Tim Ripley

Windrow & Greene

Published in Great Britain in 1994 by
Windrow & Greene Ltd.
19A Floral Street
London WC2E 9DS

ISBN 1-872004-99-7

Published in the USA by
Specialty Press Publishers
& Wholesalers Inc.
11481 Kost Dam Road
North Branch, MN 55056
(612) 583 3471/ fax 583 2023

The author wishes to thank the following
individuals and organisations for their
help in the preparation of this study.

Mark Ritson, BAe Dynamics; MSgt Rolf
Carter, PAO, USAF Development Test
Center, Eglin AFB; Cdr Swift,
Ordnance Officer, USS *America;* Public
Affairs Office, USS *America;* Public
Affairs Office, USS *Theodore Roosevelt;*
David Farnell Photographic, Lancaster;
Ken Carter, OSD-PA Still Media;
McDonnell Douglas; Daryl Stephenson;
Eric Hehs, Editor *Code One,* Lockheed
Forth Worth Company; Bob Walker,
DoD Still Media Depository, Anacosta;
Photo researchers, US National
Archives, Washington DC; Lt Jim
Fallon and Pat Toombs, Office of the
Chief of Naval Information,
Department of the Navy; 142nd Turkish
Air Unit; Capt Mike Rien and Iris Reiff,
PAO 52nd Fighter Wing, Spangdahlem
AB; Hughes Missiles; IDF Spokesman
Unit, Tel Aviv; Matra Defence; Texas
Instruments; John Ford, GEC Ferranti;
Lt Mark McCaffrey, NAS Sigonella;
LTC Janice Witt and Maj Steve
Headley, PIO AFSOUTH, Naples;
SIRPA/ECPA, Paris; LTC Rick Oborn,
OSD-PA; Cdr Mike Smith, USNR;
Lt Cdr Scott Sanders, USNR;
Lt Col Mike Gannon, USAF PA; Paul
Lewis, Joint Combat Camera; General
Dynamics Convair Division; United
Nations Special Commission to Disarm
Iraq; Dr Martin Edmonds, Centre for
Defence and International Security
Studies, Lancaster University.

A special credit must go to Pauline Elliot
for purging my text of grammatical chaos!

(Title page) After its success in the
Gulf War the F-117A Stealth Fighter
is now the benchmark for future
aircraft and weapons development.
(Tim Ripley)

(Above) A USAF F-111 practising low-level attack with Mk 82 high drag 500 lb bombs fitted with retarding parachutes. (US DoD)

This volume is dedicated to my father, Master Engineer 'Rip' Ripley, and his comrades in Royal Air Force Bomber Command who had to fly into harm's way with none of the electronic wizardry available to the airborne warrior of the 1990s.

Contents

Preface

This book was conceived in the months after the Coalition victory in the Gulf War against Iraq. Air power played a key role in the defeat of Saddam Hussein's war machine, thanks largely to the superbly accurate 'smart' weapons available to western air forces.

In many ways the quest to develop these smart weapons mirrors technological advances that have transformed the post World War Two world. The same microchips that drive home computer games also guide 'smart' bombs to their targets.

The author asks, however, that readers bear in mind that when a 'smart' bomb hits its target people die. 'Increased accuracy', 'lethality' and 'reliability' are really euphemisms to say that weapons can kill more people at a greater rate than before. Technological advances in weaponry may not be for the ultimate good of mankind.

Tim Ripley
Lancaster
April 1994

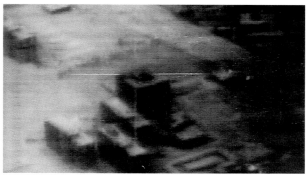

(Above right) Video tape imagery from F-117A strikes on Baghdad stunned the world. (US DoD)

(Right) Out in the desert and on the roads of Kuwait and southern Iraq, Coalition air power devastated Saddam Hussein's army. USAF Chief of Staff General Tony McPeak claimed, 'This was the first time in history that a field army has been defeated by air power.' (US DoD)

(Left) Supply of bombs to the Coalition air forces during the Gulf War became an industrial process. Demand often out-stripped supply! These are 750 lb M-117Ds destined for B-52s. (US DoD)

5

The Quest for Accuracy

Man began planning to use aircraft as weapons of war long before the Wright Brothers made the first flight in 1903. Much fun is now poked at those early airborne warriors who tossed home-made bombs out of the cockpits of their biplanes or conducted aerial duels with pistols at 5,000 feet above the World War One trench lines. But as aviation technology progressed, so did the design of airborne weaponry. Early military fliers quickly realised that accurate and reliable weapons were needed to secure victory in the skies.

From World War One onwards the development of aircraft and of airborne weapons did not always progress at a matching pace. At times some air forces have found themselves at a major disadvantage because their opponents have stolen a march

(Above) A B-52 Arc Light strike over South Vietnam in 1966. By this stage in the war some 8,000 tons of bombs a month were being delivered against Vietcong targets. (USAF/US National Archives)

(Left) The results of Operation Forest Fire – a USAF experiment to burn away the Vietnamese jungle, and hence the cover for Vietcong operations, with massive incendiary strikes by B-52s. (USAF/US National Archives)

(Both right) The quantum leap in accuracy achieved by modern smart bombs is demonstrated by this pair of USAF before and after aerial reconnaissance photographs taken during Operation Linebacker II in December 1972. (USAF/US National Archives)

on them in a particular field of aviation or weapons technology. Today we are seeing the logical progression of this process with warplanes and their ordnance being designed as integrated weapons systems.

Up until the end of World War Two the variety of airborne weapons was fairly limited, with three main classes in use: guns, free flight (that is unguided) rockets, and unguided or so-called 'iron' or 'dumb' bombs. Hitler's scientists in particular experimented with guided missiles and bombs, but these were never a major factor in the war.

Only with guns could the airborne warrior of World War Two guarantee an air-to-air kill. Rockets and iron bombs were far from accurate when striking at targets on the ground. Even with sophisticated optical sights, such as the famous Norden bomb sight, accuracy was dependent on inputting appropriate settings for the wind, barometric pressure, aircraft speed, turbulence and a host of other factors, difficult to measure in any circumstances and near impossible in wartime conditions. Even if the bomber could get through enemy air defences, there was no guarantee that its ordnance would land anywhere near the intended target.

For the British and the American air forces this problem had major implications for their strategic bombing policies. Both their governments and populations looked to them to take the war to the heart of Nazi Germany and Imperial Japan. By smashing the Axis industrial base the air force leaders hoped to deliver a knock-out blow to finish the war without major land combat. The ignominious failure of early British and American raids on Germany forced a change of plan.

The quest for accuracy was largely abandoned, in reality if not always in official statements, in favour of mass saturation raids. Hundreds, and in some cases thousands of bombers were sent to attack individual targets in the hope that if they dropped enough bombs in the general area some would hit vital parts. The RAF added its own variations to this theme, using incendiary bombs to set whole cities on fire. The aim here was to put German industry out of action by 'dehousing' its workers. In the Pacific the USAAF developed this black art to a high degree, burning the heart out of Tokyo and other Japanese cities with conventional weapons in 1945. The atomic bomb raids against Hiroshima and Nagasaki were the culmination of this policy.

HANOI THERMAL POWER PLANT
BEFORE

HANOI THERMAL POWER PLANT
AFTER

The dawn of the computer age in the years after World War Two transformed the capabilities of airborne weapons. With the outbreak of the Cold War and its accompanying arms race, a twin track of weapons development was begun and has since continued on both sides of the Iron Curtain. Huge resources were devoted to developing both new nuclear and new conventional weapons. This study will concentrate on the recent developments in non-nuclear conventionally-armed airborne weapons.

Thanks to the intensity of the East-West arms race, no stone was left unturned in the quest for airborne weapons that had a longer range, had more deadly warheads and were more accurate than those possessed by the 'enemy'. As supersonic jet aircraft rolled off production lines in increasing numbers, hi-tech weapons were developed for them to use against each other and against targets on the ground – and to destroy them from the ground.

A number of other factors led to new specialist weapons being produced that could be used in conflicts 'other than all out war'. The political unacceptability of using World War Two saturation bombing tactics against cities forced western air forces to look to highly accurate so-called 'smart weapons' as a means to wage war from the air. New strategies and tactics were required to utilise these weapons to their best advantage. 'Victory through air power' theorists saw these new smart weapons as a means to strike decisively at the heart of enemy countries, with deadly accuracy, in a way that had not previously been possible to contemplate.

The astronomical cost of modern aircraft and pilot training has also led air forces to look to develop weapons and systems specifically to protect these assets from a wide range of threats. These include missiles to destroy enemy radars and flare systems to decoy heat-seeking missiles.

Much publicity is given to smart weapons, but the world's air forces continue to place great reliance on tried and tested weapons such as guns, free flight rockets and iron bombs. However, modern technology has transformed these formerly inaccurate and unreliable items into very deadly weapons indeed.

The Cold War

The 1950s saw a burgeoning of interest in new forms of airborne weapons. To the uninitiated the early products of Cold War weapons laboratories seem very outlandish and impractical, but they were the basis of the current generation of weapons

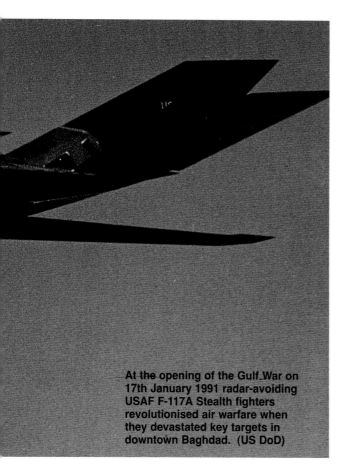

At the opening of the Gulf War on 17th January 1991 radar-avoiding USAF F-117A Stealth fighters revolutionised air warfare when they devastated key targets in downtown Baghdad. (US DoD)

missile range and would have destroyed the incoming bomber before it had the chance to penetrate friendly air space. By using missiles the interceptor would not have to close to dog-fighting range to make its kill. Or so the theory went.

A number of technological problems had to be overcome to make this system work. Radar-guided missiles could either be directed to their targets by radars mounted in the missile itself (so-called active weapons) or radars in the launching fighter whose guidance commands would be transmitted to the missile by radio. This also presupposes that the fighter itself had a radar capable of finding the target in the first place. In the early 1950s all these difficulties had yet to be properly overcome. Miniaturization of electronic components eventually allowed workable systems to be fielded in the 1960s and 1970s. By the late 1950s fighter aircraft such as the American F-4 Phantom had radars to allow them to fire early models of the semi-active AIM-7 Sparrow missile at targets beyond visual range. Semi-active missiles rely on detecting radar reflections from their targets after these have been 'illuminated' by the launch aircraft. Not until the 1970s with the introduction of the AIM-54 Phoenix missile would truly active missiles enter service. The mighty Phoenix has proved far from reliable and has yet to score a combat kill. Only in the 1990s with the entry into service of the AIM-120 Advanced Medium Range Air-to-Air Missile (AMRAAM) did active weapons reach full maturity.

Billions of dollars were thrown at smart weapon technology in the hope of achieving a decisive edge over Cold War opponents. There was no quick fix. It took many years for scientists and airmen to master the problems thrown up by these new weapons. In many ways there was an unreality about this development process. White-coated boffins easily convinced politicians and generals that science was the answer to all their defence problems. High ranking policy makers in many countries during the late 1950s claimed that the 'day of the missile' had arrived and whole air defence systems could be based around guided missiles. A generation of British, American and Russian aircraft were designed without internal guns – the missile was all-conquering. Reality would be restored over the jungles of Vietnam.

Vietnam – MiG Killing

America's involvement in the Vietnam War was the catalyst that accelerated the development of airborne weapons to their current levels of sophistication, accuracy and reliability. Unfortunately, some hundreds of American airmen died or were captured as a result of the failure in combat of the early hi-tech wonder weapons.

The first years of the American air offensive against North Vietnam were a frustrating time for

which were used to such telling effect during the 1991 Gulf War.

Cold War weapons developments in America, Britain, France and Russia all drew heavily on Nazi experimental work with guided weapons and rocket propulsion. It was advances in radars, radio communications, lasers, computers and the miniaturization of electronic components that turned 1950s scientists' wild ideas about smart weapons into ordnance that could actually be used in anger.

A closer look at the development of air-to-air missiles gives some idea of the challenges that had to be met to field effective weapons.

Air defence against strategic bombers armed with nuclear weapons was a priority for both sides during the Cold War. World War Two vintage fighters armed with machine guns or cannon were seemingly made obsolete overnight by the development of the atomic bomb. Enemy bombers had to be destroyed far from friendly territory before they had time to drop their deadly cargos. One way to do this was through the use of fighters which could fly faster than the speed of sound and which were armed with long-range radar-guided missiles. Once the enemy bombers had been detected by long-range radar, fighters would be scrambled to intercept. In a matter of minutes they would be within the US Air Force and the aviators of the US Navy. They found their missile-armed fighters were at a severe disadvantage against North Vietnam's Russian-made MiGs. The Communist fighters could turn faster and were cannon-armed and so had the edge over the Americans in close-quarter dog fights. Many American pilots had simply not been trained in air-to-air combat. They did not fully appreciate the capabilities of their missiles and so could not get into good firing positions even in situations suited to the missiles' modest capabilities. Few American pilots had fired an air-to-air missile in anything like a realistic scenario. Some even thought they had been hit when they fired their first missile in combat.

The American air-to-air missiles were also not reliable enough in operational situations. In Stateside tests the AIM-7 Sparrow achieved impressive results but over Vietnam more than 25 per cent malfunctioned. The designers did not take into account that they were often left hanging on aircraft weapon pylons for scores of sorties before they were actually fired in anger. The constant vibration of take-offs and landings caused havoc with the missiles' intricate electronics. On the other hand, the short-range heat-seeking AIM-9 Sidewinder missiles were not designed to tackle the high-G turns needed to home in on the highly manoeuvrable MiG-17s and were breaking apart in flight.

During the Rolling Thunder campaign against North Vietnam up to 1968, US fighters were only achieving a kill ratio of 2 to 1. This was nowhere near the 10 to 1 kill ratio reached in Korea. To resolve the problem the US Navy set up the famous 'Top Gun' Fighter Weapons School to teach its aircrews how to fight their aircraft and weapons to the best advantage – the process so-called of 'taking them to the edge of the envelope'. US defence contractors instituted crash programmes to rectify the defects in their products. When the air war over North Vietnam began again in earnest during Operation Linebacker in 1972 American fighter pilots quickly achieved air supremacy. The kill ratio shot up to 14 to 1.

Bombing Hanoi

In the rush during the 1950s to develop the weapons of nuclear Armageddon relatively little attention had been given to applying up-to-date technology to improving air-to-ground weapons. Only in the 1960s with the proliferation of so-called 'brush fire' wars in the Third World did the major weapons manufacturing countries turn their attention to giving conventional strike aircraft highly accurate weapons. As with air-to-air missiles, the chickens came home to roost over Vietnam in the 1965 to 1968 period when US aircraft found they had great difficulty fighting their

way through missile-based air defences to deliver bombs accurately. Casualties among the attackers were heavy and the damage inflicted was far from spectacular.

Tropical weather conditions over North Vietnam made it especially difficult to guarantee accuracy. Targets had to be attacked over and over again to achieve any probability of causing serious damage. This simply gave the North Vietnamese the opportunity to shoot down even more American planes. Unlike in World War Two, political restrictions prevented America resorting to area bombing of Hanoi and other North Vietnamese cities to overcome the lack of accuracy. Technology offered a possible solution but it would not be available quickly to turn the tide in favour of the Americans. A few dozen electro-optical (television) and laser-guided bombs were used experimentally in late 1967 and into 1968 with good results. By the time Operation Linebacker began in May 1972 they were in widespread use and achieved impressive success. Bridges throughout North Vietnam that had survived three years of bombing during Operation Rolling Thunder were dropped in days using the new smart weapons. Bombing accuracy is measured by CEP (Circular Error Probable), the average of the distance from the aiming point by which a group of bombs falls. CEPs of some 30 feet (9 metres) were possible with the new weapons, compared to previous figures of 1,250 feet (380 metres) from high flying B-52s and more than 500 feet (150 metres) from low flying F-111s.

Work on weapons specifically to counter Soviet made radar-guided surface-to-air missiles (SAMs) began as soon as these started to threaten the programme of American spy flights over the Soviet Union. After CIA pilot Gary Powers' U-2 spy plane was shot down in Soviet air space in 1960 and other U-2s were downed over Cuba in 1962 the Americans began to accelerate efforts to develop anti-radar missiles. The first operational missile was the AGM-45 Shrike which was ready in time to see action over North Vietnam in 1966. Early versions of this type proved to have major shortcomings. They had to be pre-programmed before take-off to home on a particular radar frequency; and their range was shorter than the Soviet-made SA-2, Guideline SAMs in use by North Vietnam, so the launch aircraft had to fly within range of the enemy SAM before it could engage an enemy radar.

Individual strike aircraft were also given on-board self-defence systems to protect them from enemy air defences. Radar homing and warning (RHAW) devices were installed to tell pilots when they were being tracked by enemy radar. Small electronic countermeasures pods were designed to allow enemy radars guiding SAMs or air-to-air missiles to be jammed. Flare dispensers were also fitted to decoy heat-seeking missiles by providing an

(Right) F-4D Phantoms of the 8th
Tactical Fighter Wing head for North
Vietnam at the height of the 1972
Linebacker offensives, armed with
Paveway laser-guided bombs.
(USAF/US National Archives)

(Below) A 'Gorilla Package' of
USAF F-16 fighters takes on fuel
from KC-135 tankers before heading
for targets deep in Iraq. (US DoD)

alternative heat source away from the aircraft for the missiles to chase.

The North Vietnamese were expert at using night time as a sanctuary to allow them to move troops and supplies along the famous Ho Chi Minh trail into South Vietnam. To defeat the night America devoted vast resources to creating effective night vision systems for attack aircraft. Infra-red and low-light television were the primary systems developed and by 1972 these were deployed on a good number of aircraft in South East Asia.

The accuracy problems with iron bombs forced America to look for weapons that could deal with large 'area' targets, such as truck parks, artillery and SAM batteries, supply dumps and infantry formations. A series of cluster bombs was therefore introduced during the mid-1960s. These could spread hundreds of smaller sub-munitions over wide areas. By fitting delayed action fuzes they also allowed air dropped minefields to be sewn along the Ho Chi Minh trail.

A major problem was also discovered (or rediscovered) concerning the use of iron bombs by high speed aircraft flying at low level. Often there would be insufficient time for the bombs' fuzes to arm before impact. To allow time for bombs to arm after leaving the delivery aircraft, retarding parachutes or fins had to be fitted to increase the time the bombs stayed in the air before impact. This also prevented any bombs detonating prematurely and damaging the dropping aircraft.

The US Army and US Marine Corps both deployed many hundreds of helicopters to Vietnam. Initially these were often armed on an improvised basis but soon purpose-built gunship types became available. At first these were only equipped with basic machine guns and free flight rockets but more sophisticated and powerful gun and missile systems followed. By 1972 the first guided missiles had been fitted to allow the helicopter gunships to take on enemy tank units. Using wire-guided TOW missiles the first attack helicopters achieved impressive results, destroying some 40 tanks and other vehicles during the battles of Kontum in May 1972.

Other Conflicts

The American experience in Vietnam proved to be a major stimulus to the development of airborne weapons, but other conflicts also had an important influence. One of the most significant air wars of recent history was the 1967 Arab-Israeli conflict. In six days the Israeli Air Force destroyed the air forces of its Arab neighbours, largely in a series of audacious attacks against their airbases. Israeli fighter-bombers surprised the Arabs with a pre-emptive strike and caught many aircraft parked in the open, where they were bombed, rocketed and strafed by cannon fire.

The first country to take notice of the dramatic Israeli victory was the Soviet Union, which began a major programme of airfield hardening to protect

(Left & below) The bunker busting GBU-28 'Deep Throat' bomb under test at the USAF's Development Test Center during the Gulf War. (USAF DTC)

its frontline airbases in East Germany, Poland, Czechoslovakia, Hungary and the western USSR from surprise attack. Hardened aircraft shelters were constructed to protect aircraft and other vital facilities, such as bomb dumps and command posts, while runways were reinforced to prevent them being put out of action by bomb craters. Almost overnight it seemed that the Soviets had made their air forces immune to attack on the ground at least.

When NATO spy satellites spotted this crash building programme, alarm bells began ringing in western capitals. A number of countries developed different weapons to defeat the Soviet concrete defences. Britain developed the JP-233 anti-runway weapon which was designed to crater runways and litter airbases with mines and other delayed-action sub-munitions. The enemy would have to devote a great deal of time and effort to clearing away the results of a JP-233 attack. The French developed the Durandal anti-runway bomb, which is rocket-assisted to give it the velocity to break open re-inforced concrete surfaces. Both the British RAF and the USAF developed special penetrator warheads for their laser-guided bombs to allow them to destroy Warsaw Pact hardened aircraft shelters — if they were able to hit them.

As NATO began to respond to the massive Soviet tank threat during the 1970s and early 1980s, it became clear that highly accurate anti-tank missiles were needed that could be used at low level and in

bad weather or at night. To ensure aircraft survivability in the face of layered Soviet tactical air defences pilots had to be able to acquire targets and launch their weapons in as short a time as possible. The fate of the Israeli Air Force over the Suez Canal in the 1973 Yom Kippur War was an object lesson in what happens when a poorly prepared air force mixes it with a Soviet style air defence system of anti-aircraft guns and missiles. Particular concern was expressed for attack helicopters which needed to maintain a line of sight contact with their targets while the guided missiles they had fired were in flight. During these vital seconds the firing helicopter was potentially highly vulnerable to anti-aircraft fire.

The buzzword in weapons systems became 'fire and forget' capability. The first such operational weapon was the AGM-65 Maverick air-to-ground missile. After the pilot locked the missile on to its target the missile's on-board electronics kept it on course, leaving the pilot free to take evasive action to get out of the envelope of any lurking air defence system. During the 1970s and 1980s hand held laser designators began to be issued to ground troops to allow them to mark and then direct laser-guided weapons dropped by aircraft onto their targets. All the bomb-carrying aircraft had to do was to fly into the general area and release its bombs. The ground designator would then take over the job of guidance, leaving the pilot free to make his escape.

The 1982 Falklands War and the Israeli invasion of Lebanon demonstrated that major improvements had been made in air-to-air weapons since Vietnam. British Fleet Air Arm Sea Harrier fighters using Lima model Sidewinder heat-seeking missiles achieved an impressive 82 per cent kill rate against Argentinian fighter-bombers. Through improvements in its seeker unit the missile could be fired from the front aspect of targets rather than behind as was the case with previous versions of the Sidewinder. The Sea Harriers therefore did not have to manoeuvre to a position where they were able to take shots at the Argentinians' hot engine exhausts. Israeli F-15s and F-16s achieved similarly impressive results against the Syrian Air Force over the Beka'a Valley.

In April 1986 a force of USAF F-111 strike aircraft mounted a controversial attack on the Libyan capital, Tripoli, in revenge for terrorist attacks on American targets in Europe. Of the eighteen F-111Fs that took part in the raid only four put their bombs on target. Two missed because they took evasive action to avoid defences, two aborted before dropping their bombs due to equipment failure, four aborted because they could not attack without hitting civilian areas, and six missed because of problems with their computer navigation systems or because of smoke from bombs from the first waves of the attack obscuring targets. The Tripoli raid demonstrated that no matter how advanced the weapon system being used, if a strike is not well planned and executed it will fail to achieve the desired results.

The Battle of Baghdad

When Cable News Network (CNN) broadcast live to the world from Baghdad the first American attacks of the Gulf War, modern aircraft ordnance came of age. When USAF Lieutenant General Chuck Horner showed video images from F-117A Stealth fighters of laser-guided bombs being dropped down the ventilation shafts of the Iraqi Air Force headquarters the impact was dramatic in more ways than one. In a few seconds of television time the anti-Iraqi Coalition demonstrated its overwhelming technological superiority over Saddam Hussein's hapless forces. Popular support for the war in the United States and Europe was assured. Iraq's war effort was doomed.

Back at the war, American, British, French and other Coalition airmen had a long way to go before victory was in the bag. With the lesson of Libya still fresh in their minds they set about putting the right bombs on the right targets with a vengeance.

Fortunately the Coalition air forces were considerably better prepared for war against Iraq than the USAF and US Navy had been prior to Operation Rolling Thunder in 1965. In the 43-day air offensive against Iraq the Coalition air forces employed

A dramatic illustration of the power of the AC-130 gunship. First used, as shown here, in Vietnam, these operate by circling over their objectives, employing computer equipment to ensure that their side-mounted weapons remain on target to pour a devastating cone of fire onto their victims.
(USAF)

a plentiful supply of a rich var
weapons that had been thoroughly
being put to use by highly trained

Perhaps the most important wea
vice during the Gulf War was the A
Speed Anti-Radiation Missile (HA
ond wave of Coalition aircraft to at
the opening minutes of the war, ju
F-117As, were F-4G Wild W
Prowlers and F/A-18C Hornets an
200 HARMs. In a massive strike th
launched almost simultaneously to
out blow against the Iraqi capital's
work. The following day Coali
reconnaissance aircraft recorded a
Iraqi radar emissions as the enemy s
defence system to avoid further HA

For the duration of the war Coalition aircraft were able to operate at high altitude in relative safety from Iraqi radar-guided SAMs. More than 2,000 HARMs were fired during the war, destroying hundreds of Iraqi radar sites. The HARM's range and Mach 2 speed meant it could strike targets from outside SAM envelopes and Iraqi radar operators had hardly any time to react to an incoming missile.

Some 210,800 gravity bombs weighing 84,200 tons were dropped during the Gulf War by American aircraft. They included Mk 80 series iron bombs and cluster munitions. The degree of accuracy achieved with these weapons is not clear, but it was undoubtedly better than in Vietnam. While the problems of correctly measuring wind, air turbulence, and so on were still present, modern technology had taken much of the error out of iron bombing. USAF F-111E crews for example reported CEPs of 40 feet (12 metres) when bombing from 15,000 feet (4500 metres) and CEPs of six feet (1.8 metres) when attacking at 200 feet (60 metres). This degree of accuracy was achieved through the use of computer navigation and bomb release systems. These measure and integrate the effects of wind, aircraft speed, air pressure, G-loading, altitude, rate of descent and ballistic trajectory of the bomb. Paradoxically, the success of the Coalition forces in neutralising the longer-range Iraqi missile-defence systems worked partly to the detriment of bombing accuracy. After the first few hours of the war Coalition aircraft did not usually operate at low level, normally the safest and where bomb accuracy is likely to be best, because the remaining Iraqi threat was from anti-aircraft artillery and short-range heat-seeking SAMs which are only effective at these altitudes.

To hit vulnerable soft targets, such as truck parks, radar sites, anti-aircraft missile positions, artillery sites and infantry units, cluster bombs were used in large numbers with devastating effect. Some 26,000 Rockeye II cluster bombs were used as well as thousands of the newer CBU-87/89 weapon. The Iraqis called them 'black rain' because the sky turned black when a cluster bomb opened-up over their positions. While cluster bombs inflicted heavy casualties and terrorised Iraqi units they left a horrible legacy after the war. Up to a third of the sub-munitions failed to detonate, leaving Kuwait and southern Iraq littered with deadly waste metal. Today they are still taking their toll even after a major clear-up effort by bomb disposal teams.

RAF and Royal Saudi Air Force Tornado GR.1/IDSs also emptied the contents of more than one hundred of their JP-233 anti-runway weapons on Iraqi airfields in daring ultra-low-level attacks. Contrary to popular myth no Tornados were lost while actually delivering the weapon, but crews did report it was a fraught experience. UN inspectors who visited Iraqi air bases after the war reported that they were still littered with sub-munitions months later. Indeed on the first night of the war only some 10 per cent of the 600-strong Iraqi Air Force was able to get airborne, and of that number only 24 were combat aircraft.

US aircraft delivered a total of 15,000 precision guided weapons, weighing 7,400 tons, against Iraqi targets during the Gulf War. These included laser- and optically-guided bombs, Maverick air-to-ground missiles and anti-radiation missiles.

The USAF reported that approximately 80 to 90 per cent of its laser-guided bombs landed spot on their targets. Thousands of key Iraqi installations were destroyed in the war, including headquarters, command bunkers, bridges, communications towers, arms factories, hardened aircraft shelters, runways, tanks, artillery pieces and aircraft in revetments.

If Coalition intelligence could find a target then ordnance could be delivered against it, even in bad weather or at night thanks to the infra-red night-vision systems available in aircraft such as the F-117A, Tornado, F-15E or F-111E. As events in Tripoli had shown, it took great skill and good planning to take advantage of the effectiveness of the latest generation of smart weapons.

Targets could be hit with relative impunity but the Coalition experienced problems in actually destroying hardened Iraqi command bunkers. Saddam Hussein had buried some of his bunkers so deep that the USAF I-2000 and British penetrator bombs could make no impression on them. The USAF then began a crash programme to develop

the 4,700 lb (2,115 kg) GBU-28 'Deep Throat' penetrator bomb. This monster weapon saw action on the final day of the war.

In the deserts of Kuwait Coalition aircraft stalked Iraqi tanks and artillery with great determination. The big armour killers were the USAF's A-10A Warthogs, which fired some 5,000 Maverick missiles with up to an 80 to 90 per cent hit rate. Confirmed Warthog kills with all weapons included 1,106 trucks, 987 tanks, 926 artillery pieces, 501 APCs, 249 command vehicles, 112 buildings, 96 radars, 72 bunkers, 51 Scud missile launchers, 58 AAA sites, 11 FROG missile launchers, nine SAM sites and two air-to-air helicopter kills (with guns). A-10A pilots reported they could hit targets at some five miles (8 km) range with the Maverick while flying at 10,000 feet (3000 metres), which is slightly less than the advertised range but enough to give a good stand-off capability. Only five A-10As were lost out of some 8,755 sorties flown.

In the one-sided air battle between the USAF and the Iraqi Air Force, the radar-guided AIM-7M Sparrow missile at last proved its worth, claiming 24 confirmed kills and one unconfirmed kill. Heat-

The Hughes AIM-54 Phoenix missile is the primary long-range air defence armament of the US Navy's F-14 Tomcat fighters. The Phoenix is one of the most advanced (and hence most expensive!) air-to-air missiles ever developed. As of early 1994 it had yet to claim a combat kill. An AIM-54C is shown being fired. (Hughes/US DoD)

seeking AIM-9M Sidewinders were used to down a further 12 Iraqi aircraft.

All the missile kills of the war fell to USAF F-15C Eagles which, thanks to the support of E-3 AWACS radar aircraft, were able to engage targets at beyond visual range. Eagle pilots reported that Iraqi pilots often behaved as if they had little idea they were being stalked by American aircraft. The bugs in the Sparrow had long been ironed out so they worked as advertised, first time round. The Iraqi Air Force did not know what had hit it.

Almost two years after the end of the Gulf War the new AIM-120 AMRAAM showed its capabilities when two Iraqi fighters fell to the new smart air-to-air missile during a brief clash between Iraqi and western forces. The USAF later used it over Bosnia in February 1994 when a Serbian bomber was brought down by an F-16C inside the United Nations No Fly Zone. Three other Serbian jets fell to Sidewinders in the same incident.

Future Weapons
Weapons designers have not rested complacently on their laurels since the end of the Gulf War. After largely satisfying the quest for accuracy, the aim of weapons designers in the 1990s is to develop weapons that can be delivered from outside the envelope of enemy defences, to cut down friendly casualties. Costly low level raids on Iraqi airfields during the Gulf War showed the vulnerability of manned aircraft. The need for aircraft to overfly their targets is being reduced by the introduction of more effective stand-off weapons.

After the success of the F-117 Stealth fighter, this new technology is also slowly being incorporated into aircraft weapons. This is to prevent the presence of the launch aircraft being given away to enemy radar when their bombs are released.

The logical conclusion of these trends would perhaps seem to make the manned aircraft obsolete. We have already seen the United States turn to sea-launched Tomahawk cruise missiles as its weapon of preference for its strikes against Iraq in 1993. Nevertheless, success in war still clearly depends on the human characteristics of bravery, ingenuity, dogged determination and imagination. Machines have none of these. The airborne warrior is not yet redundant.

Iron Bombs

A US Navy F/A-18 Hornet 'pickles' a pair of Mk 84 2,000 lb 'iron' bombs over the Fallon Ranges in Nevada. Every US Navy carrier air wing goes to Fallon to sharpen up its bombing accuracy before embarking on an operational cruise. (McDonnell Douglas)

On the face of it the design of the basic 'iron' or 'dumb' bomb does not seem to have advanced much since World War Two. Indeed the American Mk 80 bomb series, which will soldier on into the next century as the primary weapon of scores of air forces around the world, was designed back in the late 1940s.

The forward section of an iron bomb normally contains the explosive charge, activated by a fuze which is usually placed at the nose of the bomb casing. Indeed the nickname 'iron' bombs comes from the rough and ready metal casings formerly used in their manufacture. Fins at the rear of the bomb stabilize its flight after release. There are three principal methods of dropping weapons of this type. There is firstly the basic 'straight 'n' level' approach where the launch aircraft simply flies over its target and drops its bombs down onto it. At high altitude this is the least accurate method of delivery because the bombs can easily be forced off target by failure to allow correctly for wind and other factors. Dive bombing ensures greater accuracy because the launch aircraft flies its bombs directly at the target before weapon release, giving less opportunity for the influences of nature. Toss or lob bombing involves a pilot putting his aircraft into a dive or sharp turn and then pulling up just before releasing his bombs. This passes on the momentum of the aircraft to the bomb which then arches up before dropping on target. By using this tactic the launch aircraft does not have to overfly its target.

Considerable advances have been made, however, in the accuracy and lethality of iron bombs. For some years now aircraft ordnance has normally been carried on the external stores stations or pylons of jet fighter-bombers or attack helicopters. The days of large bombers with big bomb bays seemed largely to be over. This meant that modern bombs needed to have good aerodynamics not only for accurate delivery but also while being carried by the launch aircraft. To complicate matters these characteristics are not necessarily the same. A new feature is the need for bombs to share the radar-avoiding stealth characteristics of their launch aircraft. The F-117 gets around this problem by returning to the traditional design of an internal bomb bay.

As the Argentinians found out to their cost in the Falklands conflict, low level delivery requires bombs with fuzes that can arm themselves after only a few seconds in the air. Thanks to their Vietnam War experience the Americans have developed a series of weapons with parachutes and extendable fins to slow down their rate of descent. This allows the bomb's fuze to arm itself properly before impact. The use of retard parachutes also helps stabilise bombs released by fast moving jets. Low flying jets create a swirling vortex of air behind them which can force bombs off target.

Fuze technology has also advanced considerably to allow for detonation precisely on impact, at pre-determined altitudes, or after penetrating the target, depending on the effect to be achieved. A final option is for delayed action long after the bomb has hit the ground. This makes it very dangerous and difficult for the enemy to clear up the mess after an air raid.

The war load of fast jets has been made considerably more effective by the development of what are termed ejector racks. These allow multiple loads of bombs to be carried on a single pylon. On release they spread the bombs away from each other and allow a good impact pattern.

The relatively poor accuracy of iron bombs has been a significant factor in encouraging many air forces to invest in cluster weapons. These dispense

(Above) A B-52 unloads its deadly cargo over South Vietnam during a high altitude Arc Light strike. (USAF/US National Archives)

(Left) In 'high-threat' environments USAF B-52 crews train to hit their targets from ultra-low level, necessitating the use of Mk 82 500 lb high drag bombs fitted with retarding parachutes. These allow the bomber to escape from the area before the bombs explode and give the bombs' fuzes time to arm. (US DoD)

(Right) The B-52 school of gentle diplomacy... (Tim Ripley)

B-52 STRATOFORTRESS
We're probably near you at one of our ten convenient locations nationwide

We Provide
Precision Bombing
Strategic Deterrence
Peace Through Strength
Victory Through Devastation
Urban Renewal

668 BMS GRIFFISS AFB NY
WE MAINTAIN THE BALANCE

We Destroy
Armies
Military Industrial
Complexes
Political Centers
Air Bases
The Enemies Will
To FIGHT

668TH BOMB SQUADRON
When you care enough to send the very best

large numbers of small, but deadly, sub-munitions over a large area. American forces first used dispenser units mounted on their aircraft in Vietnam. The first CBUs were activated by timers so they had to be dropped at specific altitudes to produce the optimum dispersal pattern. Finding this made aircraft vulnerable to enemy fire, cluster bomb units (CBUs) were developed which could be dropped like iron bombs. Modern cluster bombs have radar fuzes to control the height of release of the sub-munitions so toss bombing can be used to launch them towards their targets, protecting the launch aircraft from much enemy fire.

Cluster bombs can be filled with a wide range of sub-munitions such as anti-personnel, armour piercing, incendiary or mines. The potential of cluster bombs in sowing minefields was recognised

long ago. Air dropped mines are now very sophisticated and include magnetic, pressure and booby-trap weapons.

Britain and Germany both still use large dispenser units on their Tornado strike aircraft but the Gulf War experience has led to great efforts being put into developing stand-off dispenser weapons.

Much work is also under way to develop so-called 'smart sub-munitions' or sensor-fuzed weapons which use infra-red sensors to seek out large hot metal objects such as tanks. A CBU is used to seed them over an enemy tank column and while they descend by parachute their seeker units are looking for suitable targets. Once they have found a target they will then fire themselves at the vulnerable top armour of the enemy tank.

(Both left) Rockeye II CBU-59 cluster bombs contain some 717 deadly BLU-77 anti-personnel or anti-material sub-munitions. Here, a US Navy A-6 is using three of the weapons to take out an Iranian patrol boat. (US Navy)

(Top) The Rockeye cluster bomb is easily distinguishable by its long thin shape and usually its white paint. (Tim Ripley)

(Above) Developed by France, the Matra Durandal anti-runway weapon was used against Iraqi airfields in the Gulf War by French and American air forces. (Matra)

(Left) 500 lb Mk 82 bombs, the workhorse of the USAF for some 40 years, on a A-10A's triple ejector rack. (Tim Ripley)

(Above) Cluster bombs such as this French-made Belouga were used during the Gulf War to seed Iraqi airfields with delayed action sub-munitions to hinder attempts to repair bomb damage. (US DoD)

(Left) The CBU-89 CEM (Combined Effects Munition), seen here under the port wing of a refuelling USAF F-16C over northern Iraq, is the most modern cluster bomb in the USAF inventory, containing some 202 sub-munitions. (Tim Ripley)

(Below) The British Royal Air Force and Fleet Air Arm field their own distinct series of 1,000 lb iron bombs, as shown on this Sidewinder-equipped Jaguar. (Tim Ripley)

Guided Missiles

USAF AGM-86C conventionally
armed Air Launched Cruise Missiles
(ALCM) have a range of over 1,762
miles. In a trans-Atlantic raid seven
B-52Gs fired 35 ALCMs at Iraq in
the opening hours of the Gulf War.
(US DoD)

The British Aerospace Active Sky
Flash missile is typical of the
current generation of 'fire and forget'
air-to-air missiles. An on-board radar
guides the missile to its target.
(British Aerospace Dynamics)

(Below) Britain's Tornado F.3
fighter relies on a mix of Active
Sky Flash and Sidewinders.
(Tim Ripley)

(Bottom right, sequence) 'Splash
One!' An AIM-120 AMRAAM scores
a kill during test firing.
(USAF)

Guided missiles can be directed towards their targets by on-board guidance devices or by commands transmitted by radio, wire or laser light beam. These are fully fledged smart weapons and they give the user great control and accuracy, but they do not come cheap.

Air-to-air guided missiles come in two main classes: radar-guided and heat-seeking. The first radar-guided missiles relied on commands transmitted by radio but advances in computer and sensor technology mean they can now be fully independent. These are termed semi-active and active missiles. Missiles that depended on radio links for control were vulnerable to enemy jamming and the firing aircraft had to keep the target in its radar envelope. If the target, for example, was able to shield itself behind a mountain then the radar would 'lose the lock' and the missile would 'go stu-

pid' or out of control. The firing aircraft would also usually have to keep heading straight towards the target, and perhaps into greater danger, while the missile was in flight

Active missiles have their own on-board radar system which makes it more difficult for the target to get away. However, this considerably increases the cost of the missile. The firer also has to be very sure that the target is hostile before firing his missile and this may not be straightforward, especially when the target is beyond visual range. Once fired it is almost impossible to call off an active radar-guided missile.

Heat-seeking missiles contain an infra-red heat detector or seeker unit that homes in on a target's hot areas, such as engine exhausts. These are the ideal weapons for close-quarter dog fighting. Because they are attracted to aircraft engine areas a

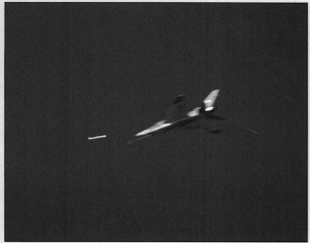

USAF F-15 Eagles go into battle with a mix of radar-guided AIM-7 Sparrows (on fuselage) and heat-seeking AIM-9 Sidewinders (under-wing) to give their pilots a good range of kill options. (Tim Ripley)

A Sidewinder heat-seeking missile streaks away from an F/A-18 Hornet towards a target drone on a test range. The AIM-9 is the most successful air-to-air missile ever developed, with scores of kills to its credit in every major air combat since the 1960s.
(McDonnell Douglas)

hit is usually catastrophic for the target. Modern heat-seekers are very manoeuvrable and advances in their seeker units allow them to differentiate between real targets and decoy flares.

Air-to-ground guided missiles come in a variety of forms. The hottest property at the moment are cruise missiles. These can be strategic weapons with ranges measured in many hundreds of miles. They are computer-guided, aided by real-time up-dates from navigation satellites. They have digital map memories and terrain-following radar systems to allow them to penetrate deep into enemy territory and strike within meters of their intended target. The launch aircraft may not even have to fly into enemy air space.

For tactical use against targets such as tanks, artillery and supply dumps, more responsive weapons are needed to cope with moving targets on a rapidly changing battlefield. So-called first generation weapons required the operator to guide the missile to its target by means of radio commands or command signals sent down fine wires that were spooled out behind the missile in flight. These could only be used from the ground or slow moving helicopters which made the operator vulnerable to attack during the missile's flight.

Next came 'fire and forget' weapons which contained computer chips that remembered the target's location and allowed the launching aircraft to take evasive action immediately after launch. Now entering service in increasing numbers are laser-guided weapons that can be fired from out of sight of the enemy and are then guided to their target by laser designators on the ground. Next on the agenda are weapons which are fitted with millimetre-wave radars to seek out tanks on the battlefield. The ultimate in air-to-ground guided missiles are weapons that contain television or infra-red cameras in their nose. They transmit the images back to the launch aircraft some 50 miles (80 km) away, from where the pilot or crewman can 'fly' the missile to its target.

For anti-ship operations radar-guided missiles are in general use. Like active air-to-air missiles they contain on-board radars that identify their targets.

One of the most important types of missile in use today is the anti-radar or anti-radiation missile. These home in on enemy radar or radio signals. Some nations use them offensively to open the way through enemy air defence systems for strike aircraft. In naval warfare they are almost a substitute for radar-guided anti-ship missiles. Warships, particularly large vessels such as aircraft carriers, have literally scores of electromagnetic emitters, with radar, radio and other electronic systems in virtually constant use. They are sitting ducks for anti-radiation weapons.

A Sidewinder blasts away from an
F-15C Eagle during a test firing
exercise. (USAF DTC)

The AIM-9 Sidewinder has been
sold around the world and many air
forces, including those of the
former Eastern Bloc, have copied it.
(Tim Ripley)

Hanging on a Russian MiG-29 are
two Vympel R-73 heat-seeking
missiles (Sidewinder equivalents,
NATO codename AA-11, Archer) and
a semi-active radar-guided Vympel
R-27 (Sparrow equivalent, NATO
codename AA-10, Alamo).
(Tim Ripley)

(Left) This French Army Aviation (ALAT) Gazelle is used as an anti-helicopter platform, armed with up to four Matra Mistral heat-seeking missiles. (Matra)

(Right) The key part of the Sidewinder is its infra-red seeker unit which passes guidance information to four movable forward fins. These give the missile its agility in dogfights. (Tim Ripley)

(Bottom left) All modern fighter aircraft, such as this Saab JAS 39 Gripen, must be able to field a wide range of ordnance. (Saab Military Aircraft)

(Below right) French Mirage 2000 fighters use the Matra Super 530D semi-active missile as their primary air-to-air weapon. This relies on the firing aircraft's radar to guide it to its target. A radar fuze then detonates the warhead. (SIRPA Air)

(Above) Taking over from the AIM-7 Sparrow is the new AIM-120 Advanced Medium Range Air-to-Air Missile or AMRAAM (shown on the two inboard pylons). It brings many of the features of the AIM-54 Phoenix into a weapon almost the same size as a Sidewinder. To the time of writing F-16s fielding the AMRAAM have notched up six kills over Iraq and Bosnia. (Tim Ripley)

(Left) Loading Sidewinders onto an F/A-18 aboard the carrier America. (Tim Ripley)

(Left) The AGM-65 Maverick is one of the most successful air-to-ground missiles ever developed, with more than 5,000 being used during the Gulf War. A kill rate of over 90 per cent was recorded. Here one is being loaded on to an A-10A Warthog. (US DoD)

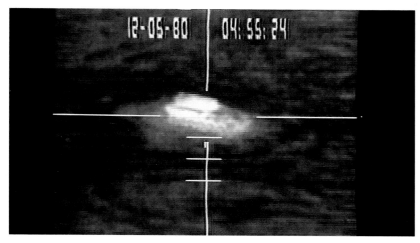

(Top right) A Warthog pilot's view of a target seen through the infra-red sighting system of Maverick. (Hughes Missiles)

(Right) Looking death in the eye – a Maverick just before impact. (US DoD)

(Below) Impact. The power of the Maverick warhead is vividly demonstrated. (US DoD)

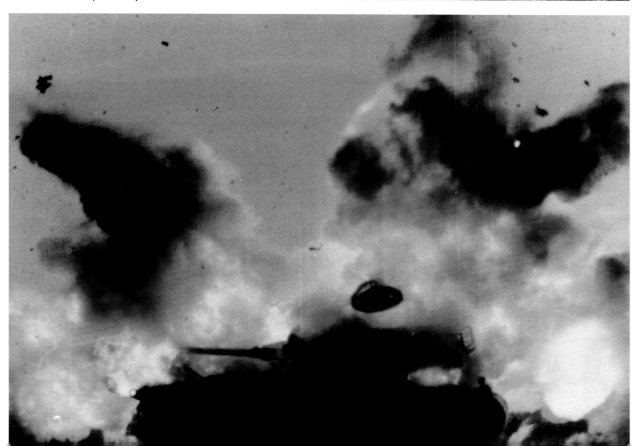

The AGM-84E Stand-off Land Attack Missile (SLAM), launched here by an A-6E Intruder, allows the aircraft crew to 'fly' the missile to targets at up to 86 miles range, using real-time transmissions from an infra-red video camera in the nose of the missile. It was first used to great effect during the Gulf War.
(US Navy)

(Below, sequence) A Tomahawk impacts on a test target after a flight of over 400 miles. The Tomahawk carries a 1,000 lb warhead when it is conventionally armed as here. (US DoD)

For strategic strikes the Tomahawk Land Attack Missile (TLAM) BGM-109 can hit targets with pin-point accuracy at ranges between 800 and 1,500 miles. The US Navy TLAM can be fired from ships and submarines or launched from A-6E Intruders. (McDonnell Douglas)

(Above) A Hellfire is launched from an Apache attack helicopter during development tests for the missile. (Rockwell)

(Top right) The AGM-114A Hellfire uses laser guidance to achieve this degree of accuracy when fired from AH-64A Apache attack helicopters. (US DoD)

(Left) Russian-made air-to-ground missiles tend to be bigger than their Western counterparts. This Kh-31A/P (NATO designation AS-17, Krypton) anti-ship and anti-radar missile is comparable with the western Harpoon and HARM. (Tim Ripley)

(Right) Most other attack helicopters rely on wire-guided anti-tank missiles such as the TOW carried – in quad launchers – by this Italian A129. (Tim Ripley)

The USS Stark (FFG-31) burns after being hit by two Iraqi-fired Exocet anti-ship missile in an incident in May 1987. (US DoD)

The French-made Exocet put modern 'smart' weapons on the map when one of the missiles fired from an Argentine Super Etendard aircraft devastated HMS Sheffield during the Falklands War. (Tim Ripley)

(Left & right) The British Aerospace Sea Skua missile fired from Lynx helicopters proved to be an impressive combination in the Falklands and Gulf Wars. (British Aerospace Dynamics)

(Left) The remains of a Soviet-made Fan Song radar after an Israeli Air Force anti-radiation missile strike. The Israelis were in the forefront of developing missiles to defeat Soviet-made air defence systems. (Israeli Defence Force)

(Right) Over 2,000 AGM-88 HARMS were fired during the Gulf War, destroying large numbers of Iraqi radar sites. (Tim Ripley)

(Bottom left) HARM kill markings from the Gulf War on an F-4G Wild Weasel of the 52nd Tactical Fighter Wing. (Tim Ripley)

(Below) Missiles such as the HARM are now an important part of every modern air force's inventory. The launch aircraft here is an F-4G Wild Weasel. (Texas Instruments)

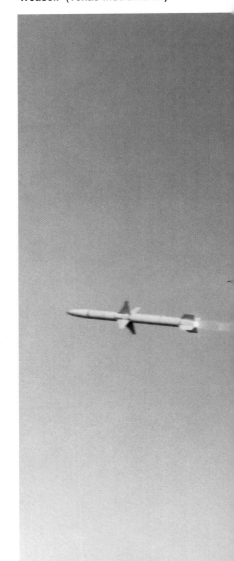

An M113 APC about to be obliterated by a Paveway II laser-guided bomb during a test.
(US DoD)

Guided Bombs

(Right, sequence) The GBU-15 is an electro-optically guided 2,000 lb bomb, which allows the weapon to be 'flown' to its targets by a crewman in an aircraft out of range of enemy air defences. (US DoD)

uided bombs are halfway between iron bombs and guided missiles but, although they are unpowered gravity weapons, they are often mistaken for fully fledged smart weapons because of the way their guidance systems are able to modify their flight paths towards their targets.

Some weapons of this type are manufactured as a single item but most come in the form of kits, with nose and tail fins and a guidance unit, that are attached to standard iron bombs. Guidance is either by electro-optical or laser systems. Electro-optical systems have television cameras or infra-red sensors in the noses of the bombs which transmit images back to the launch aircraft. Laser systems rely on designators that illuminate the target with a laser beam.

Not surprisingly, putting guided bombs on targets is a complex business. First the launch aircraft has to toss the bomb into the 'basket' or its guidance unit will have too much work to do to correct the bomb's trajectory and keep it on target. The 'basket' is a notional cone-shaped area with its apex at the target. Once successfully in the basket the guidance unit of the bomb is activated. In the case of laser systems a seeker unit in the nose of the

bomb will pick up the laser light reflected off the target and then ride down the beam to the impact point. Computers in the seeker unit move the fins on the bomb to keep it on the right trajectory.

All the systems on the launch aircraft and the bomb will have to work first time because if they fail at any time during the bomb's flight it will simply revert to its natural 'dumb' ballistic trajectory and may not land anywhere near the target. In the case of electro-optical systems the launch aircraft must stay within communications range of the bomb during the flight, which can be difficult if the enemy defences are active. Aircraft that are designating targets for laser-guided bombs have to stay in line of sight of the target. For the early systems used in Vietnam this meant that the launch aircraft had to fly almost straight and level in full view of any enemy defences, which was not a healthy prospect. Modern systems mount laser designators in automated turrets that keep the system aligned with the target no matter what evasive action is taken by the designating aircraft. Finally, poor weather can play havoc with both types of systems. Low cloud or smoke can obscure targets making it impossible for the operators of electro-optical sys-

tems to identify their correct aim point. Cloud, smoke or haze can also interfere with the reflection of laser light and throw the bomb off target.

To overcome these problems new means of providing guidance are being looked at. One way to increase the survivability of the launch aircraft is to fit rockets to the guided bomb. These can boost the lob range of the bomb so the launch aircraft does not have to penetrate so far into enemy air space.

Experiments are also taking place in the USA to use satellite navigation systems to provide precise guidance to bombs. Before launch the pilot inputs the co-ordinates of the target into the bomb. Once in the 'basket' the bomb will receive constant updates transmitted from a Global Positioning System (GPS) satellite to correct its trajectory. Accuracy to within 10 feet in all weathers is the objective of the exercise.

Guided bombs started out in the 1960s as an inexpensive, interim solution until guided missile technology had matured. Since then they have become the standard precision weapon of many air forces. Even though they have their limitations compared to guided missiles their comparative cheapness means they are here to stay.

(Above) The Paveway series of bombs is constantly being upgraded by the manufacturer, Texas Instruments, to improve its accuracy and reliability. The weapon on the inboard pylon is a Paveway II series GBU-10 2,000 lb weapon. Compare the seeker unit with that of the Paveway III series GBU-24 2,000 lb bomb in the foreground. (Tim Ripley)

(Left) CP-123/B Paveway II 1,000 lb bombs before being loaded onto RAF Tornados during the Gulf War. (GEC Ferranti)

(Right) US Navy Intruders regularly use the Paveway II GBU-12 500 lb weapon for anti-shipping sorties and strikes against air defence sites. (Tim Ripley)

(Top right) The view through the British TIALD (Thermal Imaging and Laser Designator System) equipment before and after a 1,000 lb bomb impact. (GEC Ferranti)

(Below) Almost 500 Iraqi hardened aircraft shelters were ripped apart by American, British and French guided bombs during the Gulf War. Special penetrator bombs easily cut through the shelters' roofs and exploded inside, blowing their doors across the deserts, as seen here at Al Salman air base in southern Iraq. (SIRPA/ECPA France)

(Left) French Jaguars in the Gulf used Matra 400 kg BLG (Bombes à Guidance Laser – laser-guided bombs) in conjunction with Atlas designator pods, together seen here under the port wing and centreline of this Jaguar. (SIPRA AIR)

(Right) The AVQ-26 Pave Tack laser target designator pod fitted underneath an F-111F bomber. Like the TIALD system it allows computerised tracking of targets while the aircraft manoeuvres. (Tim Ripley)

(Below left) The GEC Ferranti Thermal Imaging and Laser Designator (TIALD) pod mounted on an RAF Tornado. A computer stabilization system allows the seeker unit and designator to track targets automatically while the aircraft manoeuvres to avoid enemy air defences. (GEC Ferranti)

(Below right) British Buccaneers used AVQ-23A Pave Spike pods to 'buddy designate' for RAF Tornados on many raids into Iraq. (Tim Ripley)

Rockets

A pair of Hornets in action with rockets over the Fallon ranges. (McDonnell Douglas)

Rockets were the first powered stand-off airborne weapons to be developed and saw considerable service during World War Two with all the major air forces in ground attack, tank hunting, maritime operations and other roles, even including air-to-air use. They not only allowed the launching aircraft on occasion to avoid overflying the enemy position but also, if fired as a salvo, had a 'cluster' effect on the target. The psychological impact on the enemy of seeing a salvo of rockets incoming was also not to be underestimated.

Trained pilots became quite skillful in their use, but their rudimentary aiming prevented their being very effective tank killers. In the post-war era the devotion of vast resources to smart weapons meant that free-flight rockets were neglected for a time.

It was during the Vietnam War that they made a big comeback, initially as a target-marking system. Fast moving strike aircraft had considerable problems identifying targets in the jungles of South East Asia, so forward air control (FAC) aircraft started to carry rockets for target indication. When they spotted a target a white phosphorous rocket was fired at it and the approaching waves of strike aircraft then bombed on the fire at the rocket's impact position. Rockets were also fitted with flares to illuminate targets at night. In the Gulf War USAF F-16s and A-10s, along with USMC OV-10s and F/A-18Ds, used similar tactics to pin-point targets for strike aircraft. RAF Jaguars also put rockets to good use against Iraqi ships.

For attack helicopters rockets provide a useful area weapon. American Huey Cobra and Apache helicopters sport rocket pods which, when fired en masse or in ripple sequence, can devastate area targets. Fragmentation warheads which contain 2,200 anti-personnel flechettes (dart-like sub-munitions) provide a means to put a stop to mass infantry attacks.

(Right) An AH-64A Apache attack helicopter puts down suppressive fire with its Hydra 2.75 inch rockets. (US DoD)

(Left) Russian helicopters are well supplied with rockets to help support air assault landings. In addition to the other weapons being displayed, the Kamov Ka-50 Werewolf (NATO codename Hokum) can carry four B-8W-20 rocket pods, which each contain twenty 80 mm S-8A/M anti-tank or fragmentation warhead rockets. (Tim Ripley)

Rocket mountings need to be aerodynamically designed, like this Russian UB-32A-24 pod, otherwise they can cause unwelcome drag and degrade the launch aircraft's performance. (Tim Ripley)

US Marine Corps F/A-18D Hornets
maintain the FAC rocket tradition,
marking targets for following waves
of attack birds. This Hornet has four
LAU-97 rocket pods which each
carry four 5 inch Zuni rockets.
(McDonnell Douglas)

The AH-64 Apache usually carries two 19-round M261 rocket pods on its outer weapon stations. (Tim Ripley)

The First Lady

Guns

An AC-130 Spectre on the prowl.
(US DoD)

ew modern fighter jocks would consider going into battle without some sort of gun on their aircraft. For all the hi-tech wizardry of guided missiles or bombs, the gun offers a reliable weapon of last resort. It is not vulnerable to enemy electronic counter measures or completely disabled by computer bugs. If you can see the target and it is in range, you can try to blast it with your gun.

Modern fighters sport either heavy 20 mm to 30 mm single barrel cannons that fire high explosive shells, or multi-barrel Gatling-type guns to fill the sky with lead. Helicopters mount a variety of cannons and machine guns, with transport machines fielding rifle-calibre machine guns for self-protection, and attack helicopters using large calibre guns to hunt tanks, other ground vehicles and other helicopters.

Single barrel cannons are getting rarer these days but still pack a considerable punch. They predominate in fighter aircraft and give pilots close range options in situations where missile shots are tricky.

The premier Gatling-type gun must be the 30 mm GAU-8 Avenger on the US Air Force's A-10A Warthog. It combines the hitting power of larger calibre weapons with the rate of fire associated with multi-barrel designs.

Small calibre Gatlings or Miniguns are common on helicopters and they give crews the ability to spray a 'hot LZ' with fire power. Attack helicopters such as the Apache and Cobra sport cannon systems with sophisticated sights and advanced infrared vision systems to give them a night combat capability.

While modern combat aircraft are all generally fitted with internal guns, some older designs of aircraft still in service, such as the F-4 Phantom and Harrier, have had to be fitted with external gun pods.

The heaviest calibre weapons carried by any modern combat aircraft are mounted in the AC-130 Spectre gunship. This converted C-130 Hercules transport aircraft boasts a variable weapons fit that can include a 105 mm howitzer, a 40 mm cannon, two 20 mm cannons and two 7.62 mm Miniguns. These weapons fire sideways out of the fuselage. Computer aiming systems allow the aircraft to circle over a target, keeping the weapons correctly aimed, and almost literally obliterate it. Sophisticated night vision equipment also helps make the Spectre a formidable all-weather and night attack platform.

(Above right) Russian Tupolev Tu-25 (NATO codename Backfire) bombers carry twin radar-controlled 23 mm GSh-2-23 tail cannons – shades of World War Two B-17 Flying Fortresses! (Tim Ripley)

(Above, far right) Not surprisingly the Russians are keen on cannons in their Mil Mi-24 helicopter gunships (NATO codename Hind). Some have four-barrelled Jak B-127 Gatling guns (12.7 mm calibre) in nose turrets as shown here, while others have fixed twin 23 mm GSh-2-23 or 30 mm GSh-2-30 cannons for anti-tank work. (US DoD)

(Right) Fixed helicopter cannons are something of a Russian speciality. Kamov Ka-50 Werewolf (NATO codename Hokum) attack machines feature two A42 30 mm cannon and carry 500 rounds internally. (Tim Ripley)

(Left) While modern AC-130s bristle with electronic wizardry, their largest weapons still have to be loaded by hand, like this massive 105 mm howitzer round. (US DoD)

USAF Special Operations Forces MH-53J helicopters use GAU-2B/A 7.62 mm Miniguns to put down suppressive fire on 'hot LZs'. (US DoD)

Gunship aircraft with side-mounted weapons proved very effective at providing close air support in Vietnam. The gunships circled the target and poured fired onto enemy positions just as the modern Spectre types are tasked to do. (US DoD)

US Army Apache attack helicopters made short work of Iraqi tanks and other armour with their Hughes M230A1 30 mm Chain Guns during the Gulf War. The weapon is slaved to the helicopter gunner's or pilot's helmet sight so that he aims the weapon simply by looking at the target. (Tim Ripley)

A close up of the A-10A's GAU-8 Avenger cannon. The rider depicted in the nose art seems to have an Avenger tucked under his arm but in fact the gun and its ammunition drum are together about the size of a small car. (Tim Ripley)

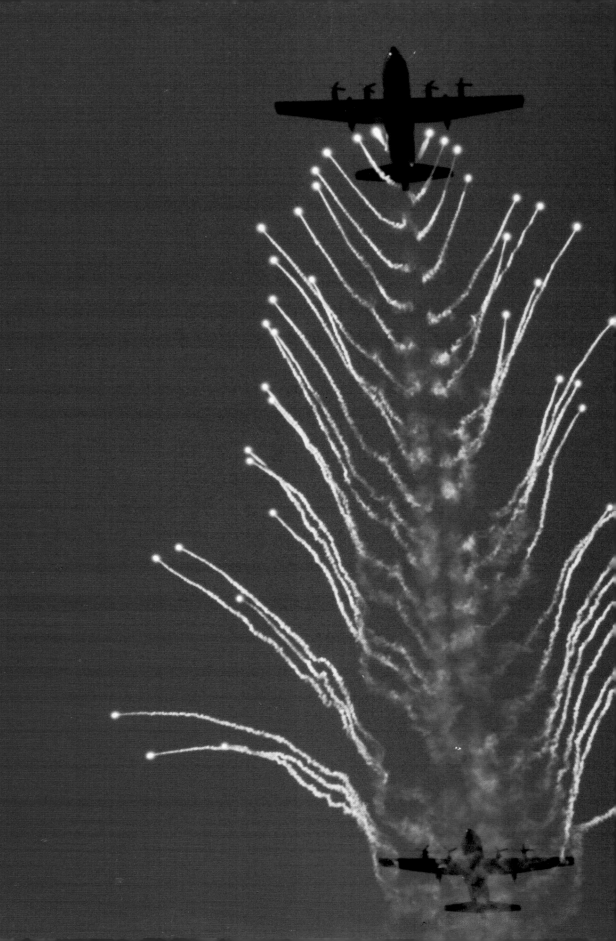

Pods

Modern combat aircraft carry a wide range of specialised night vision systems, electronic jamming devices, flares and chaff to decoy missiles in add-on pods carried on weapon pylons or bolted to their airframes. As the operational life span of an aircraft type is now many years, rather the one or two years that was the case in World War Two, there needs to be flexibility to allow constant upgrading to take place. It is therefore unusual to see any modern combat aircraft that does not sport pods, bumps or blisters containing some sort of hi-tech defence system.

To defeat radar-guided missile threats jamming pods are regularly carried by strike aircraft on one of the stores stations or pylons. Warning devices are also now standard. Pod mounting this equipment allows defence systems to be changed to meet specific or new threats more readily than if it was internally fitted. Dispenser pods are also used to fire clouds of chaff to confuse enemy radars.

Heat-seeking missiles need different countermeasures, including devices for detecting enemy launches, flare dispensers to fire decoys, and infrared generating equipment to confuse missile seeker units.

Flare and chaff dispensers come in many shapes and sizes. Some are linked to automatic missile detection systems and others can be fired manually. The latest flares are designed to burn in a way that is invisible to the naked eye. This prevents the flares so clearly giving away the location of the aircraft to the enemy . Dispensers can also be mix-loaded with chaff and flares.

To improve the attack capability of older combat aircraft podded night vision and laser designation systems have been developed. The most common of these systems are known as forward looking infra-red (FLIR), which allow attack aircraft to operate by night as they would in daylight. Some FLIR pods can be integrated with laser designators to allow laser-guided bombs to be used at night.

A key role for combat aircraft is aerial reconnaissance but few air forces can afford to dedicate aircraft to this specialist role on a permanent basis. Photographic reconnaissance pods are an increasingly important way of achieving this capability.

Flare defence systems like those deployed by this US MC-130E aim to decoy heat-seeking missiles away from their intended targets by providing alternative heat sources for the missiles to home on and follow. (US DoD)

Low flying aircraft and helicopters find it difficult to manoeuvre to avoid heat-seeking missiles so flare defence systems are vital if they are to operate successfully in a high-threat environment. The photograph shows a French Puma helicopter employing the Matra Saphir defence system during the Gulf War. (SIRPA AIR)

US Marine Corps CH-53Es were some of the first helicopters to be fitted with flare dispensers to counteract enemy shoulder-launched heat-seeking missiles such as the Russian-made SA-7 Strela. (US DoD)

The Soviets were quick to deploy flare defence systems on their helicopters after the Americans and British supplied heat-seeking missiles to the mujahedin in Afghanistan. (Tim Ripley)

An alternative to flare defence systems are infra-red decoys or 'disco lights', such as this AN/ALQ144, which transmit light pulses to confuse a heat-seeking missile's guidance systems. (Tim Ripley)

Fast jets need flare and chaff dispensers, like this Bofors BOZ-101 pod, that have as little adverse effect on performance as possible. (Tim Ripley)

(Opposite) Turning night into day is the role of thermal imaging devices, such as the TADS/PNVS turret mounted in the nose of the AH-64A Apache attack helicopter. (Tim Ripley)

(Left) Vintage US Navy A-6E Intruders were kept in top fighting form from 1978 onwards with the retro-fitting of AN/AAS-33 TRAM (Target Recognition and Attack, Multi-sensor) turrets, which combine forward-looking infra-red and a laser designator. (Tim Ripley)

(Below left) The view through a TRAM system as an A-6E moves in to refuel from a KC-135 tanker during the Gulf War. (US DoD)

(Below) The AAS-35 Pave Penny laser spot tracker system used on the A-10A is not to be confused with laser target designators used with laser-guided bombs. The Pave Penny is intended to allow forward air controllers on the ground to 'mark' targets in confused battle-field situations for approaching A-10s. An on-board computer then projects the target position into the pilot's head-up display (HUD) allowing for highly accurate iron bombing or Maverick missile shoots. (Tim Ripley)

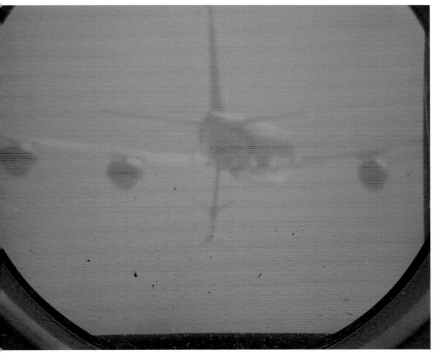

(Above) The US Navy's current Tactical Aerial Reconnaissance Pod System (TARPS) can be fitted to standard weapons pylons on F-14 Tomcat fighters. (US DoD)

(Above right) This TARPS photograph, taken during the Gulf War by an F-14 of VF-84 from the USS Theodore Roosevelt, shows the infamous 'Highway of Death' near Kuwait City. (US Navy)

(Right) To give combat aircraft their own on-board jammers, electronic warfare pods are now common. This example on an A-10 is an AN/ALQ-131(V) which is optimized to deal with specific surface-to-air and air-to-air missile threats. (Tim Ripley)

(Bottom right) American-made AN/ALQ-101 (V) jamming pods are in widespread use with allied air forces. This pod is mounted on an RAF Gulf War Buccaneer. (Tim Ripley)

(Left) In the electronic war the US Navy EA-6B Prowler's ALQ-99 Tactical Jamming System has a key role. It transmits very strong signals which can blank out enemy radar screens over hundreds of miles. (Tim Ripley)

Special Weapons

In spite of all the effort put into developing smart bombs and missiles there are occasions when they cannot do the job.

When American helicopter crews asked for a device that could instantly create jungle landing zones in South East Asia they got the M-121/B-11 'daisy cutter' or 'big mother'. This was a left-over from World War Two and boasted a 10,000 lb warhead. A special fuze was fitted to guarantee an overground detonation to produce a huge pressure wave and clear the site by blast. The bomb was too bulky to be dropped by any combat aircraft so it had to underslung from a large helicopter or pushed out the back of a C-130 Hercules on a pallet. A parachute was then deployed to slow its descent to allow the drop aircraft to escape from the danger zone.

By the time of the Gulf War the USAF had replaced the old M-121 with the BLU-82 which weighed in at 15,000 lbs. Anyone within a one mile radius when one of these explodes will suffer fatal internal injuries. Major organs and arteries are literally crushed by the massive overpressures. Bodies of victims at first appear uninjured but closer examination reveals massive bleeding from every orifice. Unless under cover, anyone at up to three miles range will suffer serious injuries. Coalition troops who entered target areas after eleven BLU-82s were dropped on Iraqi positions reported finding large clumps of bodies near the impact points. After a few days in the open all trace of blood had disappeared from the corpses leaving them strangely unmarked. Some BLU-82s were used to detonate paths through minefields, but others were used as terror weapons to undermine Iraqi morale in key areas of the front line. One BLU-82 was dropped on an Iraqi truck park, reportedly leaving 4,500 dead. Three BLU-82s were dropped almost simultaneously on an Iraqi-held island, killing or seriously injuring every one of its 1,000-strong defence force.

To give naval forces the ability to sow minefields at long range, air droppable mines are now in widespread use with naval air forces. Using magnetic and sound detonation devices they can lie undetected underwater for a prolonged period until they arm themselves, a ship passes over, and then they explode.

Chemical weapons have a pedigree that goes back to World War One and before, but it was not until the Cold War that they were widely developed as aerial weapons. Both East and West developed large inventories of chemical bombs and delivery devices. These included large bombs and dispensing devices similar in principle to crop-spraying systems.

In Vietnam the US used C-123 aircraft to spray agricultural defoliant on jungle areas in an attempt to destroy the foliage used by the Vietcong to hide their positions. On a number of occasions the Americans also dropped CS riot gas grenades from helicopters and light aircraft to break up Vietcong 'human wave' attacks.

The first ever documented airborne attacks with lethal chemical weapons took place during the 1980-88 Iran-Iraq War. Iraqi dictator Saddam Hussein had at least five types of chemical bombs produced and used, some which were copied from Soviet and western designs, others of which were indigenously developed. They contained mustard and nerve agents.

Spray systems were also reportedly fitted to Iraqi light aircraft and helicopters. Artillery-delivered agents were used frequently against Iranian troop positions, and air-dropped chemical weapons were pressed into action against rebel Kurdish towns and villages in areas inaccessible to Iraqi troops. Some 5,000 Kurdish civilians were killed when waves of Iraqi aircraft bombed the town of Halabjah with scores of nerve agent bombs.

(Above left) Few modern combat aircraft can carry an M-121/B-11 or a BLU-82, so in Vietnam they had to be dumped out the back of C-130 Hercules transports or carried by heavy lift helicopter such as this CH-54 Sky Crane.
(US National Archives)

(Left & right) The 10,000 lb M-121/B-11 'Big Mother' area weapon in action in Vietnam to clear jungle from a landing zone or new fire base position. In the Gulf War the modern day version, the 15,000 lb BLU-82, was reserved for special missions at key points along the frontline.
(USAF/US National Archives)

(Above) ADM-141 Tactical Air Launched Decoys (TALD) have the radar cross section of large bomber aircraft. On the first night of the Gulf War scores were dropped by US Navy aircraft to fool Iraqi air defence commanders into activating large numbers of their radar sites so that AGM-88 HARM anti-radar missiles could destroy them. (US DoD)

(Above right) A Spanish design was copied by the Iraqis to produce their LD-250 mustard agent bomb, which contained 64 litres of this gas. (United Nations/H. Arvidsson)

(Right) Some 150 litres of mustard agent was contained in each of these Iraqi AALD-500 bombs. Strike aircraft and helicopter gunships were used to deliver these weapons during the Iran-Iraq War from 1980 onwards.
(United Nations/H. Arvidsson)

(Left) USAF C-123s spray Agent Orange defoliant on the Vietnamese jungle. (US National Archives)

Ordnance Men

A Paveway II GBU-16 1,000 lb laser-guided bomb kit being assembled on a US Navy A-6E Intruder. (US Navy)

REMOVE BEFORE FLIGHT

Putting bombs on target is not just down to the skill of pilots and weapon system operators sitting in the cockpits of strike aircraft. Back at base highly trained personnel are required to prepare and load the bombs correctly and safely on to the right aircraft at the right time. These are the ordnance men, or 'ordies' as they are known.

Their work is physically demanding. Heavy missiles or bombs sometimes have to be manhandled up on to aircraft and cannon rounds are fed into magazines by hand-operated machines. To get aircraft fully bombed up often requires ordies to work through the night on exposed flight lines, in all weather conditions from desert heat to rain and snow. Ordies on aircraft carriers have to cope with the noise and danger of flight deck operations in close proximity to jet aircraft.

Skill is also required. Modern smart weapons are complex items which need highly trained personnel to maintain and load them. Some smart weapons come complete in user-friendly containers; others, such as laser-guided bombs, need to be constructed from kits by skilled personnel.

Fitting fuzes, even to comparatively simple iron bombs, is an equally important job. If not set properly the bombs may be dangerous to their owners and will certainly not work as advertised, exposing an aircraft and pilot to enemy fire for nothing.

The safe loading and storage of ordnance is of vital importance. Modern western ordnance has built-in safety features, including fuze pins and pylon pins to prevent weapons being prematurely fired on the ground. These pins are removed at the 'last chance' point just before take-off so no accidents can occur as the aircraft is taxiing around the flight line. To prove to the pilot that his aircraft's weapons are ready for action, the ordie holds the pins up above his head in clear view of the cockpit.

After a number of accidents on US Navy aircraft carriers in the 1960s, western ordnance now features other safety features including an applied coating of fire-retardant, rough, ablative material to prevent explosions in the event of fire. The best defence against accidents is the presence of skilled personnel who know the safety rules concerning ordnance and stick to them.

Preparing ordnance for action is a time consuming job. Putting together a laser-guided bomb kit, for example, can take anything from twenty minutes to six hours, depending on the complexity of the weapon and the manpower available. On aircraft carriers this problem is made worse by the restricted access to the ship's magazine – unlike a bomb dump at an airbase where the ordnance can be laid out in neat rows. To overcome this problem, weapons are pre-loaded onto carriers in packages tailored to the combat scenarios anticipated.

In time of war ordnance men may not have to face enemy fire to the fullest extent, but they share the emotions of the pilots and aircrew who do. In the Gulf War ordies enthusiastically painted kill and mission symbols on the sides of their aircraft. When their aircraft failed to come home they sometimes felt guilty. Did their plane get shot down because something went wrong with its weapons? On two occasions Coalition aircraft were lost because bombs prematurely exploded in flight. An aircraft returning to base with empty bomb racks and a smiling pilot was the sign of a job well done.

(Left) A special loading system bulk feeds 20 mm cannon ammo into an F/A-18C Hornet aboard the USS America. (Tim Ripley)

(Right) A US Marine Corps ordnance handler puts the finishing touches to a Paveway II GBU-16 1,000 lb laser-guided bomb kit. (USMC)

Giant Mk 84 2,000 lb iron bombs
arrive at a Gulf War F-16 flight line
on a flat bed truck, from where
they are down loaded on to an
erector/tractor vehicle to be taken
to their individual aircraft. (US DoD)

USAF ordies move a Paveway III
GBU-27 into position before loading
into an F-117A's weapons bay
during the Gulf War. (US DoD)

(Above) Even though these blue-painted Mk 76 training bombs on a USS Theodore Roosevelt F-14 Tomcat are inert, the ordnance man is still going through the proper pre-flight safety checks. (US DoD)

(Left) Final checks to an AIM-9 Sidewinder by a Red Jacket on the USS Theodore Roosevelt. Flight deck personnel aboard carriers wear differently coloured jackets according to their duties to make supervision easier and operations safer. (US DoD)

(Right) These Paveway II GBU-12 500 lb laser-guided bombs on board the USS America have been coated in heat-retardant material to prevent them exploding in a fire. This is a safety measure introduced after a number of catastrophic accidents on US Navy carriers in the 1960s. (Tim Ripley)

(Below) A solitary Red Jacket appears among a mixed-squadron group of F-18s on a carrier deck park. (Tim Ripley)

(Both right) Red Jackets aboard the America manhandle a Sidewinder onto the starboard outer weapon station of a Hornet as unconcerned air crew pass by. The physical difficulty of this task in bad weather can clearly be imagined. (Tim Ripley)

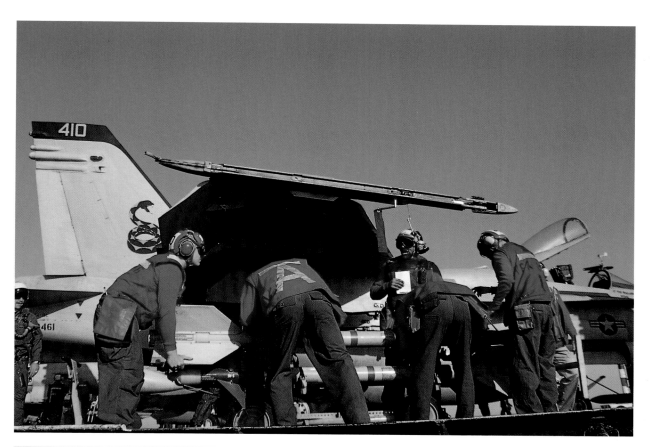

(Above) Careful adjustments to an F-16's load in the early morning before a Gulf War mission. (US DoD)

(Left) Fighter ordnance men use a Linkless Ammunition Loading System (LALS) to arm the 20 mm cannon of an F-14 Tomcat aboard the USS Independence. (US Navy)

(Right) Routine maintenance on a Sidewinder. Weapons have to be regularly serviced if they are to work as advertised. (US DoD)

(Left) The final checks on a 1,000 lb bomb being loaded on to a US Navy A-6E Intruder before a mission over Iraq. (US Navy)

Future Weapons

In laboratories around the world scientists are hard at work designing the airborne weapons of tomorrow. No stone is being left unturned to develop weapons that are cheaper to buy, more destructive, easier to use, have longer range, or are more difficult to detect and counter.

Some designs are simply progressions of existing weapons and many have been mentioned earlier in this study. Other new weapons are radical departures from existing ideas.

The USAF has already put its battle-winning Stealth technology to use on the AGM-129 advanced cruise missile carried on B-52 heavy bombers. This can fly some 1,800 nautical miles (3,340 km) without being detected by enemy radar. This technology is also being put into use on shorter range missiles, including the experimental AGM-137 Tri-Service Stand Off Attack Missile (TSAAM). Britain and France both have similar concepts of missile under development, although it will be many years before they see service.

Air-to-air ordnance looks set to become even more deadly, with active missiles being given their own on-board electronic countermeasures to defeat enemy jamming. Multi-capable weapons with heat-seeking and radar guidance are not that far away.

The US has successfully tested, but not fielded operationally, an anti-satellite missile that is designed to destroy targets in outer space.

Amid the continuing race to develop airborne weapons of war, one event occurred recently that put the science of destruction to more constructive use. Concerned about the accuracy of the food air drops over war-torn Bosnia, USAF experts turned to the cluster bomb school of ballistics to develop a new method of delivering relief food supplies. Called the TRI-wall Aerial Distribution system (TRIAD), it is basically a heavy duty cardboard box filled with hundreds of emergency ration packs. It is pushed out the back of a C-130 Hercules at 15,000 feet. Just like a cluster bomb it breaks open at precise altitude, scattering its contents over the target zone. After being tested on a bombing range in Germany the system was used extensively over Bosnia with superb results. The crews now call their C-130s 'food bombers'.

(Below) Radar-defeating Stealth technology has already been incorporated in the design of the AGM-129 Advanced Cruise Missile. (US DoD)

(Right) The 2,000 land miles range of the AGM-129 gives the USAF an unprecedented global reach. Few air defence systems could stop an attack by these Stealth weapons. (US DoD)

(Left & below) The Dispenser Weapon System 39 has a similar role to the old JP-233 runway attack weapon but is a stand-off system so attack aircraft do not have to overfly heavily defended airfields. It is shown in flight with a Sidewinder-armed Saab JAS 39 Gripen. (Saab-Scania)

(Right) The French Apache Stealth cruise missile is at an advanced stage of development, including radar cross section testing. (Matra)

(Below right) The TRIAD or 'cardboard food cluster bomb' used to supply besieged Bosnian towns. (Tim Ripley)

(Bottom right) Two TRIADs exiting from the rear ramp of a C-130 during a test mission. (Operation Provide Promise/JIB)

Glossary

Modern military aviation is a subject littered with abbreviations and specialist vocabulary. Aircraft ordnance has a language all of its own. By providing a glossary of official designations, radio jargon and other commonly used terms it is hoped to help the uninitiated to make more sense of the subject.

AAA: Anti-Aircraft Artillery or Triple A

AAQ: Designation for airborne infra-red, special type, can be a target system or pod

ACM: Air combat manoeuvring or dog fighting

AGM: Air-to-ground missile (official US designation prefix for various types)

AIM: Air intercept missile (official US designation for air-to-air missiles)

ALE: Designation for airborne countermeasures, ejection which usually take the form of flare dispensers

Alpha Strike: All out bombing effort from a US Navy carrier

ALQ: Designation for an airborne countermeasures, special purpose, pod or installation

AMRAAM: Advanced Medium Range Air-to-Air Missile (AIM-120)

ASM: Air-to-surface missile

AVQ: Designation for airborne visual system

AWACS: Airborne Warning And Control System

AXS: Designation for airborne television system

BAI: Battlefield air interdiction or strike against enemy troops on or just behind the front line such as reserves or command posts

BDA: Battle damage assessment or study of the results of an air strike

BLU: Generic NATO term for Bomb Live Unit, referring to any type of live bomb

Bogey: Unidentified aircraft

Boola-Boola: Radio call confirming destruction of airborne target drone

Boresight: To align the barrel of a gun precisely with its sight

Buzzer: Radio call signifying enemy jamming of communications system

BVR: Beyond visual range

CAP: Combat air patrol or fighter patrol

CAS: Close air support or air strike in support of troops in contact with enemy forces

CBU: Cluster bomb unit (US designation)

CEP: Circular error probable, the measurement of ordnance accuracy

Chaff: Radar decoy material, usually taking the form of small pieces of metal designed to appear on enemy radars as if they are large aircraft or missiles

DACT: Dissimilar air combat training, dog-fight training with a type of aircraft similar in performance to likely enemy types

Dumb Bomb: see *Iron bomb.*

ECM: Electronic countermeasures, equipment designed to jam enemy radar or radio systems

Envelope: The limit of flight parameters of a pilot, aircraft or weapon, e.g. the maximum range or tightest turn possible

E-O: Electro-optical

ESM: Electronic support measures, equipment designed to detect enemy radar systems

Flares: Projectiles designed to decoy heat-seeking missiles by burning at high temperatures.

FLIR: Forward looking infra-red, a form of night vision system

Fox-1, 2, 3: US Navy jargon for Sparrow, Sidewinder and Phoenix missile shots, respectively

GBU: Guided bomb unit (US designation)

Gorilla: Large formation of aircraft

Grape: An easy target

HARM: High-speed Anti-Radiation Missile (AGM-88)

HERO: Hazard of electromagnetic radiation to ordnance, can cause bombs to explode prematurely

HUD: Head up display, used to provide pilot with target information

Ironhand: Vietnam term for US Navy anti-SAM missions

Iron Bomb: Unguided bomb, i.e. not powered or directed in any way other than by gravity and other natural influences

Judy: Aircraft has visual or radar contact with correct target

LGB: Laser-guided bomb

82 Laser, 84 Laser: US Navy slang for Paveway series LGBs

LLTV: Low-light television, a form of night vision system

Magnum: USAF Gulf War era term to signify launch of a HARM

MER: Multiple ejector racks, a type of American bomb rack

No Joy: Pilot does not identify a bogey

NVG: Night vision goggles

OHO: Ordnance handling officer, responsible for moving ordnance on a US aircraft carrier

Ordie: Ordnance man

Parrot: Military IFF transponder, used to indicate if an aircraft is friend or foe

Pave: Precision Avionics Vectoring Equipment, used as part of the code term for various LGB systems

PGM: Precision guided munition, refers to both guided missiles and bombs

Pickle: Code word for release of ordnance

Playtime: Amount of time an aircraft can stay on task

Red Shirt: Ordnance man on US Navy aircraft carriers, refers to colour of uniform shirt

RIO: Radar intercept officer, backseater in F-4 and F-14, USN equivalent of USAF WSO

ROE: Rules of engagement, determine when an aircraft has permission to open fire

SAM: Surface-to-air missile

SEAD: Surpression of (i.e. by attacks on) enemy air defences

Secondary: Follow-on explosion after initial impact of a weapon

Shooter: Aircraft that can use ordnance

Shotgun: US Navy term to signify launch of anti-radiation weapon

Skip it: Do not attack, cease intercept

SLAM: Stand-off Land Attack Missile

Sortie: Single flight by an aircraft

Splash: Enemy target is destroyed

Strobe: Enemy radar illuminating your aircraft

TALD: Tactical air launched decoy

Tally Ho: Sighting of a bogey or bandit

Tank Plinking: Gulf War tactic of using laser-guided bombs against individual Iraqi tanks

TER: Triple ejector rack, form of bomb rack

TI: Thermal imaging, form of night vision system

TIALD: Thermal Imaging and Laser Designator system

TLAM: Tomahawk Land Attack Missile

Wild Weasel: USAF SEAD aircraft

Winchester: Term used when an aircraft is out of bombs, missiles or gun rounds

WSO: Wizzo, weapon system operator, backseater in USAF aircraft, equivalent of US Navy RIO